The War of the Vegetables

BEGINNER

Alison Chaplin

AUTHOR
Alison Chaplin

EDITOR
Clare Gallaher

ASSISTANT EDITOR
Roanne Davis

SERIES DESIGNER
Anna Oliwa/Heather Sanneh

DESIGNER
Paul Cheshire

ILLUSTRATIONS
Woody

COVER ARTWORK
Woody

Text © 2000 Alison Chaplin
© 2000 Scholastic Ltd

Designed using Adobe Pagemaker

Published by Scholastic Ltd,
Villiers House,
Clarendon Avenue,
Leamington Spa,
Warwickshire CV32 5PR

1 2 3 4 5 6 7 8 9 0   0 1 2 3 4 5 6 7 8 9

British Library Cataloguing-in-Publication
Data A catalogue record for this book is
available from the British Library.

ISBN 0-439-01682-7

ACKNOWLEDGEMENTS

The author would like to thank Richard
Daniels for his kind assistance and
Maggie Chaplin for her ideas.

First performed in Manchester by
participants of the 'Drama and Theatre
Workshop' in March 1997. Many
thanks to them for their suggestions
of script changes and enthusiastic
performance!

For permission to give a performance
of this play at which an admission
charge is made, please contact the
Editorial Department, Educational
Books, Scholastic Limited, Villiers
House, Clarendon Avenue,
Leamington Spa, Warks., CV32 5PR.
You do not need to seek permission if
you do not charge an entry fee for the
performance. Performing licences
must be applied for prior to beginning
rehearsals.

Fees are £10.00 per performance for
a paying audience of up to 200 people
and £15.00 per performance for
paying audiences of 200 people or
over.

*Alison Chaplin is the drama consultant
for the Borough of Stockport and
manager of 'Arts on the Move', a
company specializing in providing a
range of drama and theatre services. For
information call 0161 881 0868.*

CONTENTS LIST

The War of the Vegetables

INTRODUCTION

USING THIS BOOK

The aim of each performance play is to provide teachers with the necessary resources to read, rehearse and perform short plays. This book enables teachers and children to understand the process of interpreting scripts and the approaches needed for successful rehearsals and performances. From providing pre-rehearsal support, to supplying linking reading and writing tasks, the contents are structured in a way that assumes no prior knowledge of script work and no previous experience of staging performances, leading those involved through the process in easy-to-follow stages.

WORKSHOP SESSIONS

These are provided to help teachers to introduce the children to the concept of drama, enable them to read and understand playscripts, help them to explore the implicit themes and issues within the play storyline, appreciate character development and learn the relevant skills required for performance.

Each session is structured so that a different aspect of working with playscripts is covered, using methods which are both practical and enjoyable.

PLAYSCRIPT

The playscript is organized in a simple-to-follow format, complete with full stage directions and scene changes. At the beginning of the script, following the cast list, is a brief outline of each character which provides an indication of behavioural traits and helps children to understand how that role should be performed. Most of the plays in this series are very simple to stage and require little in the way of make-up, costume or setting.

PRODUCTION SUPPORT

These notes provide practical advice to support teachers from the beginning to the end of the performance process, including holding auditions, structuring rehearsals, ideas for simple and effective staging, props, costumes and make-up and, finally, presenting professional 'curtain calls'. The ideas and suggestions have arisen from the author's own experience of directing the play and have, therefore, been generated by the knowledge of what worked at the time. However, they are not meant to be prescriptive and if teachers feel that they have the resources, time and skills to create more elaborate staging and costumes, or to approach the performance in a different way, then they should feel free to do so!

Allow these conversations to run for about a minute and then ask the children to stop talking. Now tell them to label themselves 'A' and 'B'. Explain that they must hold a conversation again, but that this time 'B' cannot respond until 'A' has finished talking, or completed a sentence. Insist that the children keep to this method of speaking and responding, as this forms the basis for most scripted formats.

Let these structured conversations run for about a minute and then ask the children to stop talking.

Invite them to give you feedback on the type of conversations they had and, on the board, write their statements and responses in the form of an 'A said' and 'B said' structure.

LITERACY SUPPORT

This section at the end of the book is directly linked to the requirements of the National Literacy Strategy *Framework for Teaching* and provides one or two suggestions for supportive tasks organized under the headings of 'Story', 'Characters', 'Theme', 'Working with playscript layout' and 'Performance-related tasks'. Again, these are not prescriptive but aim to provide teachers with examples of how the playscript can be used to generate structured literacy work.

The unique aspect of the *Performance Plays* is that their contents can be utilized in any number of ways – as a simple reading resource, to provide a basis for literacy tasks, to introduce children to the concept of performance drama, or to produce a full-scale school production – and readers should feel free to employ the contents in any way which meets their needs. However, the most important approach for anyone using this book is to be flexible, enthusiastic and prepared to 'have a go'!

GUIDANCE FOR WORKING WITH SCRIPTS

If the children haven't had previous experience of script work, it is suggested that you lead them through the following simple drama process to make them familiar with the style and concept of scripted performance.

Ask the children to find a partner and then to hold a conversation together. This could be about anything – the television programmes they watched last night, their favourite books, what they did during the school holidays, and so on.

Record only a couple of lines from each conversation, just to indicate to the children how these conversations can be recorded. Ask them to suggest how their second conversations were different from their original ones. Possible answers should include: that they had names ('A' and 'B'), that they could only speak when the other person had finished speaking, that the conversations were not as natural, that they had to think more about what they said and how they responded to their partners.

Now ask the children to join with another pair to make a four. (Odd numbers or unequal groups are also acceptable.) Again, ask them to hold an initial unstructured conversation with each other about a subject of your choosing and leave these to run for about a minute. Then instruct the children to label themselves 'A', 'B', 'C' and 'D' (match letters of the alphabet with the numbers in each group accordingly) and tell them to hold another conversation, this time imposing the same restriction – that is, that others cannot speak until another person has finished talking. Tell the children that they do not necessarily have to join in the conversation in alphabetical order.

Invite their feedback about these conversations, again asking for suggestions about how the second discussions differed from the first and, again, record their structured conversations on the board using 'A', 'B', 'C' and 'D' to indicate who speaks which line.

Inform the children that this is the way that plays are structured, that they are written records of people speaking to each other, having conversations or discussions, and that the names of the characters speaking are indicated at the beginning of each line of dialogue.

Give the children more help, if necessary, by asking them to:

● write their own conversations in scripted form, for example recording them in the 'A' and 'B' or 'A', 'B', 'C', 'D' format
● devise original conversations using the 'A' and 'B' or 'A', 'B', 'C', 'D' format
● lift sections of dialogue from familiar stories and record them in scripted form
● rewrite their own conversations using recognizable names instead of letters of the alphabet
● improvise a specific scene (for example, someone buying an item in a shop), before you record the improvisation using a tape recorder or

Dictaphone and then replay the recording for them to transpose into a written script.

The main aim is to enable children to appreciate that scripted text is simply dialogue, conversations or verbal statements written down and that the format gives a clear indication of who is speaking at any one time. Tell the children that characters may interrupt each other, but that two people will never talk at the same time during a scripted performance – lines will always be spoken in sequence.

Ensure that the children understand that, contrary to other written speech, script texts do not contain speech marks or quotation marks because the whole text is known and understood to be speech – they are therefore unnecessary.

Follow on from this exercise to reading and discussing an extract from any playscript, exploring how the text indicates who is speaking, analysing the sequencing of the speech and reaffirming the concept of characters speaking in turn.

As a final note, when reading the script in this book, ask the children to suggest what the purpose of the words in brackets or italics may be. Their answers should include: 'how characters say things', 'what characters do' and 'how characters do things'. Keep the language as simple as this initially, developing their vocabulary gradually as they become familiar with reading and understanding scripts.

NOTES ON PLAY THEMES AND ISSUES

The War of the Vegetables provides teachers with the opportunity to explore a variety of subjects and issues which arise from the playscript.

Although a gentle comedy, the play can be used to highlight the more serious issues of bullying, racism, 'being different', war and living in harmony with others. The aspect of the peas and tomatoes being a different colour, but both existing under the generic heading of 'vegetables', could lead to discussions on children's perceptions of people from other cultures and origins – and affirm that we all exist under the generic heading of 'humans'. The role of the runner beans is not only to emphasize the concept of bullies, but also to provide the chance to consider the importance of a group uniting if any of its members are threatened.

This play can also help teachers to encourage children to learn about 'living things' by finding out about seeds, germination and exploring how things grow, and should provide a great deal of material for cross-curricular work in this area.

WORKSHOP SESSIONS

These sessions should take place prior to any rehearsals or practical application of the playscript. They introduce the children to drama and theatre, develop their speaking and listening skills, generate positive group interaction, increase their levels of concentration, help to prepare them for the types of activity they will be doing during work on the playscript and develop their ability to perform confidently and effectively.

SESSION 1:
INTRODUCTORY WARM-UP

Timing: Spend no more than 10 minutes on each individual activity. The whole session should take no more than 40 minutes.

Resources: A large space (for example, the school hall), whistle, chairs (optional).

Objectives: To introduce children to the concept of drama, promote positive group interaction and to encourage them to respond appropriately to instructions.

FISHES

A PHYSICAL WARM-UP

Ask the children to sit in a circle on the floor or on chairs. Go around the circle, naming each child one of three fish names: these can be cod, haddock, plaice, for example.

Explain that when you call out one of the fish names,

all the children with that name should run in a clockwise direction around the outside of the circle and back to their place. It is a race among the fishes to return first.

The last child to return to his or her place loses a fishy life. Explain that each child has two (or three) fishy lives to lose (adapt the number according to the size of the group).

As children lose all of their fishy lives, they are 'out' and should quietly leave the circle.

Try this a few times, giving each fish name at least one go, then call the children back to the circle. Explain that this time you may call out the words 'Tide turn!' while the children are running. If they hear this, they must all turn and run in the opposite direction back to their seats.

You can call 'Tide turn!' as many times as you wish during any one run. The result is lots of changes of direction!

If chairs are used, put them away, ask the children to stand alone in a space, and move on to…

UP, DOWN, FREEZE

ENCOURAGES INSTANT RESPONSE TO INSTRUCTIONS

Tell the children that you are going to ask them to walk around the room carefully and slowly. Explain that you will then call out one of several commands to which they must respond, and that when they hear your command, they should respond immediately and correctly. Any children not responding correctly, or too slowly, will be 'out' and asked to sit aside.

Tell them that the commands and appropriate responses are:

shoulders – stand with hands on shoulders

up – stand with arms stretched into the air

one leg – stand still on one leg

turn – turn and face in the opposite direction

down – crouch down

head – stand with hands on head

go – begin walking around the room again

freeze – stand absolutely still and silent

Now ask the children to walk around the room. Select commands according to the ability level of your group, giving the 'go' command to allow children to continue to move around the room in between your commands. Name the children who are 'out' during each turn. These are the children who are the last to respond or who are not responding properly (for example, wobbling when they are standing on one leg).

Continue until you have a winner or winners and then move on to...

FREEZES

INTRODUCES PERFORMANCE SKILLS AND PROMOTES GROUP INTERACTION

Ask the children to walk around the room carefully, without bumping or touching each other, and tell them to listen out for your whistle. After a short time, blow the whistle, shout out a number and tell the children to get into a group of that number as quickly as they can. (You may wish to choose a group size that divides the class evenly.)

When they are in groups, call out the name of an object, for example a car, and tell them to make the shape with their bodies. (Or the object could be a piano, house, bed, television, teapot, castle – it is up to you, but all the children should make the same object of your choosing.)

Count down from 10 while they prepare their shapes, and on the count of 1, shout 'Freeze!' Insist on stillness and silence.

Go around looking at all the shapes. Comment positively on them, praising in particular those children who are 'freezing' well.

Tell the children to relax, and to begin walking around the room again as before. Repeat the exercise,

blowing the whistle, using another number and a different object for the 'freeze'.

Remember to praise effective freezes each time. Repeat until you sense that the children have had enough.

By the end, children should be fully aware of the 'Freeze' command and be able to respond to it instantly. The freeze method will be used again in a later session. End with…

CIRCLE

CHILDREN REFLECT ON AND EVALUATE THEIR SKILLS

Call the children back to sit in a circle. Ask them whether they enjoyed the drama session or not. Encourage them to give their opinions and reasons. What do they think they have learned and achieved from it?

This will give you an indication of any skills and knowledge gained, and can be used as a basis for developing children's abilities during additional workshop sessions.

SESSION 2:
APPROACHING THE TEXT

Timing: Spend up to 15 minutes on each activity. The whole session should take no more than 60 minutes.

Resources: Copies of the playscript (one per child) on photocopiable pages 19–35, script extracts prepared for small group reading, flip chart or board, sheet of A3 paper, dictionaries, paper, writing materials.

Objectives: To familiarize children with the play text.

SHARED TEXT WORK

WHOLE-CLASS READING OF THE SCRIPT

Sit with the children in a circle, or with them in their classroom places. Distribute a copy of the playscript to each child and retain one yourself.

If applicable, remind the children of the drama exercise they undertook on understanding scripts (see 'Guidance for working with scripts' on page 5). Tell them that now they are all going to read a play called *The War of the Vegetables*. Inform them that you will read the lines spoken by all of the characters at first, but that later you will invite some of them to read some of the lines spoken by the characters.

Ask the children to read and follow the words in the script whilst you are reading. (Read the lines only; do not mention who is speaking.)

After reading approximately one third of the script yourself, ask for volunteers to contribute by reading aloud two or three lines spoken by some of the characters. A good moment for this could be after MR and MRS JACKSON exit for the second time and PEA 3 says: 'No difference between peas and tomatoes, indeed! What do they mean, no difference?!' Ask for one or two children to volunteer to read the subsequent lines spoken by either PEA 5, PEA 1, TOMATO 4 and/or TOMATO 1. Continue to read the additional lines yourself.

Read the script together for only a short while, stopping at the stage direction which says: *PEAS 3 & 5 and TOMATOES 2 & 4 agree and begin preparing themselves for a fight.*

Continue to read the script yourself and then repeat the exercise of asking volunteers to read one or two lines aloud with you again. This could occur after the stage direction which says: *The TOMATOES and PEAS all form a group meeting away from the RUNNER BEANS.* Nominate children to read the subsequent lines spoken by either PEA 1, TOMATO 1, PEA 4, TOMATO 3, PEA 2, TOMATO 2 and/or PEA 3. Again, read the additional lines yourself.

As before, read the script together for only a short while, stopping at the stage direction: *There is a pause whilst EVERYONE thinks about this.* Thank the children for their efforts.

Read the remainder of the script yourself while the children continue to follow the text until the play reading has been completed.

Ask the children to turn to the first page of the script again, and move on to…

FOCUSED WORD WORK

EXPLORING THE LANGUAGE USED IN THE PLAYSCRIPT

Invite the children to suggest words from the text which they have difficulty in understanding; specify that these must be words which they have never seen or heard before. Write the words on the flip chart or board, working through the script quickly and recording all suggestions from the children.

Use any remaining time to provide definitions of the words. This can be achieved in a number of different ways:

● by the children looking the words up in the dictionary, working individually with teacher guidance
● by the children working in small groups, being allocated three or four words per group, and looking them up in the dictionary
● by the teacher providing the definitions of the words on the flip chart or board
● by the teacher providing the definitions of some of the words on the board or flip chart, but asking children to find out the definitions of others.

The process of defining words can be made more interesting by creating teams and allocating a team point each time a word is defined correctly.

Ensure that the words and their definitions are recorded on paper, in spelling books or in writing books. Leave any words not defined for further work at a later time, and move on to…

GROUP WORK

ADDITIONAL SMALL GROUP READING OF THE PLAYSCRIPT

Form the children into small groups of six to eight (it is advised that these are of mixed reading ability). Ensure that each child retains their playscript.

Tell the children that you are going to ask each group to read a short section of the play aloud with the others in their small group. Explain that they will be reading the lines spoken by the different characters (excluding the NARRATOR's). Allocate each group a different extract of the play to read together. Divide the script into five shorter sections as follows:

● From 'MR JACKSON: Now, then, shall I put…' to 'TOMATO 2: Well, we wait a little while…'
● From 'PEA 1: Howdy folks! Lovely day…' to 'TOMATO 2: Humans!! Freeze!'
● From 'MRS JACKSON: Oh, look! The vegetables…' to 'PEA 2: So why don't we just make the…'
● From 'TOMATO 6: Yeah, right! Lovely…' to 'RUNNER BEAN 1: They understand, don't you?'
● From 'PEA 6: Ooh! Now we're really in…' to 'TOMATO 6: Let's drain them till they drop!!'

Move from group to group, allocating the extracts and reminding the children that they must read all of the different character parts in their section of the play. (Some of them may need to read the lines for more than one character.) Ensure that roles and lines have been fairly and equally distributed among them.

Ask them to read through their play sections in their groups. Move from group to group, monitoring the readings and assisting when necessary. Allow sufficient time for all readings to be completed.

Thank the children for their efforts, ask them to stop reading, tell them to face the flip chart or board again, and move on to…

STORY OUTLINE

WHOLE CLASS REVIEWING AND CONSOLIDATING KNOWLEDGE GAINED

Attach a sheet of A3 paper to the flip chart or board. Write the heading *The War of the Vegetables* on it. Invite the children to recall the story told in the playscript, asking them to suggest sentences which provide a sequential outline of the events.

Guide their observations by asking: *What is the first important thing that happens in the play?* Record their answer on the A3 paper with a marker pen. Follow this by asking: *And what is the next important thing that happens?*

Continue in this fashion until you have the complete story of the events of the play written on the A3 paper in sequential outline form. Take a final moment to confirm with the children that all of the story of the play is recorded.

Thank the children for their contributions and retain the A3 paper for use in the following session.

SESSION 3:
EXPLORING THE STORYLINE

Timing: Spend up to 15 minutes on each activity. The whole session should take no more than 45 minutes.

Resources: A large space (for example, the school hall), A3 sheet from previous session, chairs (optional).

Objectives: To consolidate the children's knowledge of the context and content of the playscript.

STORYLINE FREEZES

PROVIDES A FOCUS FOR STORYLINE RECALL

Sit with the children in a circle. Invite them to recall the story outline of the play which they wrote at the end of the previous session. Go through the stages of the story noted on the A3 sheet of paper to confirm their recollections.

Tell them that they are now going to make different freezes which tell the story. Explain that these will include:

● MR JACKSON dropping the seeds

● the seeds growing

● the TOMATOES and PEAS arguing

● the RUNNER BEANS arriving and threatening the TOMATOES and PEAS

● the TOMATOES and PEAS uniting against the RUNNER BEANS

- the TOMATOES and PEAS living together happily.

Inform the children that you will ask them to either work alone, in pairs or in groups to make their freezes, and that all freezes will be performed in unison (as in 'Freezes' in session 1).

Ask the children to stand alone in a space. Tell them that you want them all to freeze individually in the position of MR JACKSON dropping the seeds. Give a countdown of 3, 2, 1 and, on the count of 1, command the children to 'freeze'.

After they have held their positions for a few seconds, ask the children to form small groups of six (or as near to six as is possible, according to class numbers). Tell them to make a freeze which shows the seeds growing. Give a little more preparation time, count down from 3 again and give the 'Freeze' command. Let the children hold the positions for a few seconds again and then ask them to find a partner and stand in a space.

Instruct them to make a freeze of a PEA and a TOMATO arguing. (Specify that this should not be fighting – there should be no physical contact!) Count down from 3, give the 'Freeze' command and ask them to hold the freezes again.

Now ask the children to form groups of eight (or as near as possible, according to class numbers). Instruct them to make a freeze which shows the RUNNER BEANS threatening the other vegetables. Allow extra preparation time. Give the countdown and 'Freeze' command. Tell them to hold the positions again.

Instruct the children to stay in the same groups and to create a different freeze, showing the PEAS and TOMATOES uniting against the RUNNER BEANS. Allow preparation time. Give the countdown and 'Freeze' command, and ask them to hold again.

Finally, ask the children to form groups of 12 (or as near as possible) and ask them to create a freeze which shows the PEAS and TOMATOES living happily together after the threat of the RUNNER BEANS has gone. Allow preparation time. Give the countdown and 'Freeze' command. Ask them to hold their positions briefly again and then tell the children to relax. Thank them for their efforts and move on to…

FOLLOW THAT VOICE

DEVELOPS LISTENING SKILLS USING INSTANT RECALL OF THE PLAY STORYLINE

Ask the children to lie down in a space on the floor and to close their eyes. Explain that you are going to tap a child on the shoulder and that, when tapped, the child must begin telling the story of *The War of the Vegetables*.

Tell the other children to listen very carefully to the voice and for the direction from which it is coming. As soon as they hear the voice telling the story, they must crawl slowly towards it, still with their eyes closed.

When the child telling the story is tapped again, he/she must stop talking immediately and the other children should stop moving the instant the voice stops speaking. Stress that the children must keep their eyes closed at all times!

Explain that another child will then be tapped, and should continue telling the story from the point where the first child left off. Again, the other children should move slowly towards the voice. Tap that child to stop him/her from continuing and to indicate to the others to stop moving. Tap another child to continue the story and to instigate movement again.

Continue until you have told all of the story of *The War of the Vegetables*. Thank the children for their efforts, tell them to open their eyes and sit up, and move on to…

SEQUENCE MIMES

DEVELOPS MOVEMENT SKILLS AND CONSOLIDATES KNOWLEDGE OF PLAY CONTENT

Ask the children to form groups of five to seven and to find a space in which to work. Tell them that you would like each group to mime a different part of the story of *The War of the Vegetables*. Explain that mime is movement without words or sound, and that each group will mime a different section of the story – these mimes will then be acted out in sequence, to show the whole story.

Use the story outline sheet (made in 'Story outline' in session 2) to allocate a different section of the story to each group. Ask the children to spend time preparing the mimes of their sections. Allow 3 to 5 minutes for this process, and move from group to group, ensuring that children are working productively.

When the time-limit for preparation and rehearsal has elapsed, ask all of the groups to stop working. Specify the sequential order in which the mimes will be performed. Ask each group to perform their mime, using each of the sequential outlines as a verbal prompt for the mime performances to start.

Invite the children to applaud the other groups after each mime. Continue the process until all of the mimes have been performed, and the whole story told in actions only.

Thank the children for their efforts and ask them to sit in a circle with you again. End with…

CIRCLE

CHILDREN REFLECT ON AND EVALUATE THEIR SKILLS AND KNOWLEDGE

Ask the children whether they enjoyed the drama session or not. Invite them to offer their opinions and reasons. What do they think they have learned and achieved from it? What do they feel they have done well? What could they have done better? How do they think the activities could help them when they are performing?

Ask them to confirm what they now know about the story of *The War of the Vegetables*. If any of the children are not sure about a particular part of the story outline, further work can be done in additional workshop sessions. These can also be used as a basis for developing their abilities.

Invite them to suggest what the content or focus of the following session should be. Acknowledge all responses, and explain that they will be exploring the play's characters in greater detail.

SESSION 4: CHARACTERIZATION AND ROLE-PLAY

Timing: Spend up to 15 minutes on each activity. The whole session should take no more than 60 minutes.

Resources: A large space (for example, the school hall), whistle, two toy telephones (or chairs).

Objectives: To explore the play's characters and encourage structured role-play.

FREEZE IN ROLE

INTRODUCES CHARACTERIZATION

Ask the children to walk around the room carefully, without bumping or touching each other, and tell them to listen out for your whistle.

After a short time, blow the whistle, call out the name of a character from the play, for example MR JACKSON, and tell the children to freeze instantly in position as that character. Use the instruction 'Freeze as…' giving the character's name. Remind the children that the 'Freeze' command means being still and silent. Ask them to hold their positions for a few seconds.

Walk around the room, looking at all the character freezes. Comment positively on them, praising in particular those children who are holding their positions well. Tell the children to relax and to begin walking around the room as before.

Repeat the exercise, blowing the whistle and calling out a different character's name. Remember to praise effective freezes. Repeat until the children have created at least three freezes and then move on to…

WALKABOUT IN ROLE

DEVELOPS CHARACTER MOVEMENT

Ask the children to walk around the room carefully again. Tell them that this time they should listen for you calling out the name of one of the characters from the play. Stress that it is essential that they walk in silence in order to hear your commands. Explain that when they hear you call the name, they should continue walking around the room, but in the style and manner of that character, and that, after they have walked as the character for a while, you will instruct them to 'walk as themselves again'.

Call out a character's name from the play, for example MR JACKSON, and instruct the children to 'Walk about as…', giving the character's name. Watch the children as they walk about in role, commenting positively on those children expressing the character well in their walk.

After a short while, instruct the children to walk as themselves again. Then repeat the 'walkabout' instruction using a different character from the play.

Continue until the children have walked around the room in the manner of at least three different characters from the play. Then ask the children to stop walking, thank them for their efforts, ask them to find a partner and a space in which to work, and move on to…

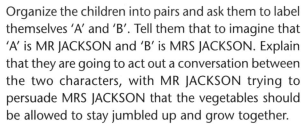

PERSUASION
EXPLORING ALTERNATIVE VIEWPOINTS AND APPROPRIATE LANGUAGE

Organize the children into pairs and ask them to label themselves 'A' and 'B'. Tell them that to imagine that 'A' is MR JACKSON and 'B' is MRS JACKSON. Explain that they are going to act out a conversation between the two characters, with MR JACKSON trying to persuade MRS JACKSON that the vegetables should be allowed to stay jumbled up and grow together.

Ask the 'B's (playing MRS JACKSON) to begin by asking the 'A's (playing MR JACKSON) why the vegetables are all mixed-up. Allow the conversations to continue for a few seconds and then instruct the children to swap roles, so that 'A' now becomes MRS JACKSON and 'B' becomes MR JACKSON.

After a few seconds, change the situation so that 'A' now becomes one of the TOMATOES and 'B' becomes one of the PEAS. Tell the children to act out a situation in which one vegetable tries to persuade the other to leave the vegetable garden. Specify that there is to be no physical contact between the two. After a few seconds, ask the children to swap roles again.

In a third situation, tell the 'A's that they are now one of the RUNNER BEANS and the 'B's that they are either a PEA or a TOMATO. Instruct the children to act out the part of the RUNNER BEAN trying to persuade the PEA or TOMATO to leave the vegetable garden. Insist on no physical contact between the two. Again, after a few seconds, instruct the children to swap roles.

During each improvised conversation, move around the room, commenting positively on the acting and in particular praising those children who are expressing their characters well. When the children have enacted each situation, thank them for their efforts and move on to...

TELEPHONE CONVERSATIONS

CONSOLIDATES VERBAL CHARACTERIZATION

Ask the children to sit in a circle. Place two toy telephones inside the circle, on opposite sides. Or, if these props are not being used, place two chairs inside the circle on opposite sides. Tell the children that you are now going to ask them to have imaginary telephone conversations.

Ask for two volunteers and place one child next to each telephone (or on each chair, in which case they should mime using a telephone). Tell the children that they are now going to make a telephone call and hold a conversation, acting as characters from the play. Give them a conversation that will allow them to speak in role. Think of one that would be appropriate or choose from the following:

● MRS JACKSON telephoning her friend to tell her about MR JACKSON dropping the seeds

● MR JACKSON telephoning the garden centre asking about what problems dropping the seeds might cause
● A TOMATO telephoning a PEA and saying how he/she feels about growing in the same garden
● A PEA telephoning a TOMATO and saying how he/she feels about growing in the same garden
● A TOMATO telephoning another vegetable and warning him/her about the RUNNER BEANS
● A PEA telephoning another vegetable and saying how frightened he/she is about the RUNNER BEANS arriving.
● RUNNER BEAN 1 telephoning RUNNER BEAN 2 and giving instructions about visiting the PEAS and TOMATOES
● RUNNER BEAN 2 telephoning RUNNER BEAN 3 and repeating the instructions from RUNNER BEAN 1.

Work through as many improvised telephone conversations as possible, continuing until the majority of children have had an opportunity to speak.

Thank the children for their efforts and (if used) put the telephones away. End with...

CIRCLE

CHILDREN REFLECT ON AND EVALUATE THEIR SKILLS AND KNOWLEDGE

Ask the children whether they enjoyed the drama session or not. Invite them to offer their opinions and reasons. What do they think they have learned and achieved from it? What do they feel they have done well? What could they have done better? How do they think the activities could help them when they are performing?

Ask them to comment on what they have learned about the characters in *The War of the Vegetables*. This could be used as a basis for future workshop sessions.

SESSION 5: CONSOLIDATING PERFORMANCE SKILLS

Timing: Spend up to 20 minutes on each activity. The whole session should take no more than 60 minutes.

Resources: A large space (for example, the school hall), copies of the playscript (one per child) on photocopiable pages 19–35, large sheet of paper and pen (optional).

Objectives: To consolidate understanding of the play and performance skills.

GROUP REACTIONS

ENCOURAGES CHILDREN TO RESPOND APPROPRIATELY IN UNISON

Organize the children into groups of ten to twelve. Ask them to find a space in which to work, and to sit or stand in their groups. Tell them that you are going to read a piece of narrative (a story describing what is happening) and that they should listen carefully and act out their reactions to what they hear (reacting with the others in their groups). Explain that they should give exaggerated reactions but that they also need to listen carefully to what is being said.

Read slowly through the following narrative, allowing the children time to react with appropriate movements and/or emotions during your reading:

It was a hot, sunny day. Mr Jackson watered his vegetable garden with his watering can. The sun shone brightly. Eventually the tomato plants began to grow slowly. They pushed through the soil and grew and grew until they were all big and strong. It felt nice to be in the warm sunlight. Suddenly the tomatoes were disturbed. Peas began to grow in between them. They grew and grew slowly towards the sun until they were big and as strong as the tomatoes. The tomatoes were very surprised to see the peas – they couldn't believe their eyes. The peas were very surprised to see the tomatoes – they couldn't believe *their* eyes. The peas wanted to live in the vegetable garden on their own and tried to get the tomatoes to leave. The tomatoes were unhappy about this and didn't want to leave the garden because they had grown there first.

The tomatoes and peas began to argue with each other. Suddenly three runner beans appeared. They were very nasty and very mean and the peas and tomatoes were very frightened. The runner beans told the peas and tomatoes that they wanted to live in the vegetable garden. The runner beans threatened to get rid of the peas and tomatoes if they didn't leave. The peas and tomatoes were very worried and afraid. They got together for a meeting to talk about what to do. They decided that they had to get rid of the runner beans and worked together to suck all of the water up from the ground. They all sucked and sucked very hard until every last drop of water had been drained from the ground. The runner beans shrunk slowly to the ground, shrivelled up and died. The peas and tomatoes were very pleased that they had saved themselves from the nasty runner beans and they all lived together happily ever after.

Praise the children for their efforts. At this point mention that this activity will have helped them to see how important it is to learn to react together on stage and that all actors should act when they are not speaking.

Ask them to remain in their groups, and then move on to…

IMPROVISATIONS

PERFORMING THE STORY IN THEIR OWN WORDS

Ask the children to sit down where they are. Tell them that you would like them to work in their groups to perform the whole story of the play, acting it out in their own words.

Let them agree among themselves who will play the different parts. Point out that there is no need to worry about not having enough people to act out all of the characters; it is more important to show what happens in the story. Their performances should not last more than 3 minutes. Tell them that when they have practised their little plays, they will be able to show them to each other.

Give them up to 5 minutes to plan and rehearse their short plays. Then ask each group to show their performance in turn. Encourage the children observing as an audience to clap after each performance. Thank all of the children for their efforts and move on to…

SCRIPT EXTRACTS

REINTRODUCES THE SCRIPT AND PREPARES CHILDREN FOR PERFORMANCE

Tell the children that you are going to ask them to act out parts of the script aloud to each other. Explain that this can entail either a simple reading or a performance that has acting and movements.

Distribute copies of the script, retaining one for yourself. Form the children into groups and allocate script extracts for performance. These can be of your own choice or taken from the following (the script extracts can be reduced or expanded to suit class size):

- Three children – the NARRATOR, MR JACKSON and MRS JACKSON (the first page)
- Four children – TOMATO 1, TOMATO 2, TOMATO 3 & TOMATO 4 (the first seven lines of their first entrance)
- six children – PEAS 1, 2, 3, 4, 5 & 6 (seven lines beginning from 'They don't look like peas…')
- five children – PEA 1, TOMATO 6, PEA 2, TOMATO 1 & TOMATO 4 (seven lines, beginning from 'Look, stop it…')
- three children – RUNNER BEANS 1, 2 & 3 (eight lines beginning from 'We don't think, we KNOW…'
- four children – TOMATO 2, PEA 2, PEA 1, TOMATO 1 (six lines beginning from 'So, what are we going to…')
- six children – PEA 3, TOMATO 4, PEA 6, PEA 5,

TOMATO 6 & the NARRATOR (from 'Let's go for…' to end of play).

The aim is to enable children to learn how to read, prepare and perform the script. Performances can be static or have movement in them, but encourage the children to use vocal expression.

Allow them up to 5 minutes to read and practise their script extracts. Then ask each group to show their pieces in sequence, according to events in the play. Invite those observing as audience members to applaud the other groups after each performance.

When all groups have performed their extracts, thank the children for their work, praise their efforts and ask them to form a circle. End with…

CIRCLE

CHILDREN REFLECT ON AND EVALUATE THEIR SKILLS

Ask the children whether they enjoyed the drama session or not. Which aspect did they enjoy the most/ the least? Invite them to give their opinions and reasons. What do they think they have learned or achieved from it? What do they feel is the most important skill they have learned?

What do they feel they have done well? What could they have done better? How do they feel about their performances? What would they change/do better if they had the chance to perform again? What do they feel is the most important thing to remember when performing in front of others? (If you wish, note their answers on a large sheet of paper to provide a visual prompt during rehearsals.)

Acknowledge all responses, thank the children for their hard work and praise their efforts.

The War of the Vegetables

CAST LIST

Narrator(s)

(option to have five narrators, each reading one verse, or any number up to five as required)

Mr Jackson

Mrs Jackson

Tomato 1

Tomato 2

Tomato 3

Tomato 4

Tomato 5

Tomato 6

Pea 1

Pea 2

Pea 3

Pea 4

Pea 5

Pea 6

Runner bean 1

Runner bean 2

Runner bean 3

18 characters *(+ 4 additional narrators if required = 22)*

SCENE

Mr and Mrs Jackson's vegetable garden

Photocopiable

CHARACTER OUTLINES

NARRATOR: speaks in verse, telling the audience what's happening in the story. Starts and ends the play.

MR JACKSON: a cheerful character who's a little bit daft.

MRS JACKSON: has a loud voice, is slightly bossy and likes her garden to be nice.

TOMATO 1: happy, a good organizer and usually likes to get on with everyone.

TOMATO 2: a bit of a moaner who can sometimes be bossy.

TOMATO 3: a little bit stupid and is always asking questions to try and find out what's happening.

TOMATO 4: a show-off with quite a bad temper.

TOMATO 5: quite lazy and doesn't like fighting.

TOMATO 6: can be rude to others and is always ready for a fight!

Photocopiable

PEA 1: cheerful and always tries to look on the bright side of things.

PEA 2: a bit lazy and can be quite nasty to others sometimes.

PEA 3: bossy, and can be quite unpleasant and aggressive.

PEA 4: a little bit stupid, asks a lot of questions but doesn't often understand the answers.

PEA 5: not very friendly and can be quite nasty towards others.

PEA 6: a bit daft and very nervous, always panics when in trouble.

RUNNER BEAN 1: the leader of the gang. Unpleasant, in control and menacing, like a gangster.

RUNNER BEAN 2: a bully. Happy to cause pain to others. Obeys Runner bean 1.

RUNNER BEAN 3: another bully! Likes to please the boss and enjoys violence.

Photocopiable

SCENE: **Mr and Mrs Jackson's vegetable garden**

The NARRATOR enters and stands facing the audience.

NARRATOR: The Jackson's had a vegetable patch, just behind their shed.
They tended it so lovingly and always planned ahead.
It fed them through the autumn, and when the springtime came,
They dug it up, they fertilized it and planted seeds again.

It wasn't such a big patch but it was perfect for their needs.
They paid it such attention, always pulling up the weeds.
They planted sprouts, potatoes, cauliflowers and watched their veggies grow;
And after all were eaten, they chose the new seeds they would sow.

One springtime, Mr Jackson was pottering in his shed,
Choosing seeds for planting, just as the gardening books said.
If he had only known then what trouble he would cause,
He'd have brought his grub at Tesco's, or the local Asda store!

The NARRATOR remains on stage.
MR JACKSON enters, carrying two packets of seeds, one in each hand. He is deep in thought as he looks at them.

MR JACKSON: *(thinking out loud)* Now then, shall I put peas or tomatoes in this little bit this year? Peas are useful for soups and with all sorts of meals, and they're yummy straight out of the pod; on the other hand, tomatoes are great in salads and for making casseroles, and there's nothing nicer to chomp on when they're fresh from the garden. Hmmm.

He holds the packets up and stands thinking again, trying to decide. Suddenly a loud voice is heard off-stage.

MRS JACKSON: *(shrieking loudly off-stage)* Brian! Cup of tea made for you!

MR JACKSON jumps violently, the seed packets fly out of his hands and the seeds spill all over the ground.

MR JACKSON: Aaah! Oh, bother! I'll just try and… *(He tries to pick up the packets and scoop up the seeds, but only makes things worse.)* Oh, well, peas AND tomatoes it is, then.

MR JACKSON exits.

NARRATOR: The seeds were scattered carelessly across the muddy ground.
Sometimes the rain fell on them, sometimes the sun shone down.
The seeds began to germinate and they very slowly grew
Until gradually, eventually, their little heads poked through.

The NARRATOR exits.
The TOMATOES and PEAS begin to enter. Each vegetable jumps in from off-stage.
(TOMATO 4 and TOMATO 6 must have another TOMATO positioned between them on stage.)

TOMATO 1:   Yo! Sunlight! Blimey, have I got a headache!

TOMATO 2:   *(to TOMATO 1)* Me too, it was a real struggle getting through that soil, wasn't it?

TOMATO 3:   *(looks around)* Wow! This is neat. Where are we?

TOMATO 1:   Dunno, looks like a nice place, though.

TOMATO 4:   *(grandly)* Okay, okay, stop panicking! I am here.

TOMATO 2:   Like we care!

Photocopiable

TOMATO 3: *(shouting towards off-stage)* Hey! You two down there, come on up, it's lovely!

TOMATO 5: *(from off-stage)* Just five more minutes.

TOMATO 6: *(shouting towards off-stage as he/she enters)* Come on, lazy bones. Why should you stay in the bed when we're all up! Move your body!

TOMATO 5: All right, all right. I was having a lovely dream... I dreamed I was being rolled in salad cream... and...

TOMATOES 1 & 6: *(shouting at TOMATO 5)* Stop right there!

TOMATO 2: *(muttering aside)* Ugh! Salad cream.

TOMATO 3: *(to the other TOMATOES)* What are we supposed to do now, then?

TOMATO 6: *(to TOMATO 3)* Don't you know?

TOMATO 4: *(to TOMATO 6)* If she knew, she wouldn't be asking, would she? Why do you have to be so unpleasant?

TOMATO 6: *(to TOMATO 4)* Because I like it.

TOMATO 4: *(to TOMATO 6)* That's no excuse.

TOMATO 6: *(to TOMATO 4)* No, but it could be considered quite a good reason.

TOMATO 4: *(to TOMATO 6)* If there wasn't a tomato between us, I'd... I'd...

TOMATO 6: *(to TOMATO 4)* Yeah? What...?

TOMATO 4: *(to TOMATO 6)* I'd... I'd... *(trying hard to think of something)*

TOMATO 1: *(to TOMATOES 4 & 6)* Oh stop it, you two. We've only just arrived and already you're arguing – give it a rest.

TOMATO 3: *(hesitantly, to the others)* So, what do we do now, then?

TOMATO 2: *(to TOMATO 3)* Well, we wait a little while for the sun to shine and then we...

He/she stops talking suddenly as PEA 1 enters.

PEA 1: Howdy, folks! Lovely day, isn't it?

ALL of the TOMATOES stare at PEA 1 with their mouths hanging open.

PEA 2: This bed's lovely – hope it's worth coming out of it! *(Noticing the tomatoes)* What the...?!

PEA 3: *(to PEA 2)* What's wrong? *(Also noticing the TOMATOES)* Oh my word! *(Shouting towards off-stage)* Hey! You lot, come up here and have a look at this!

PEAS 4, 5 & 6 enter.

PEA 4: *(staring at the TOMATOES)* They don't look like peas.

PEA 6: *(thinking aloud)* Maybe they're a new variety?

PEA 5: *(to PEA 6)* Yeah, right, a RED variety! *(To PEA 4)* They're NOT peas, stupid!

PEA 4: *(to PEA 5)* Not peas?

PEAS 1 & 2: *(irritated)* NO!

PEA 4: So, what are they doing here, then?

PEA 3: That's what I want to know. *(To the TOMATOES)* Just what do you think you're doing in our bed?

TOMATO 6: *(to PEA 3)* YOUR bed? What a nerve! We were here first, that makes it OUR bed.

PEA 3: Oh it does, does it? We'll soon see about that!

Photocopiable

TOMATO 3: *(confused)* Why have we got peas in our bed? I've never had a pea in my bed before.

PEA 2: *(nastily)* Are you sure about that?

TOMATO 1: *(to PEA 2)* And just what do you mean by that remark?

PEA 5: Well, if the stalk fits…

PEA 6: *(wailing in fear)* What are we going to do? What will become of us?!

PEA 1: *(to PEA 6)* Now don't wail. It'll be all right. We'll just grow like we're supposed to.

PEA 3: But there won't be enough room in this bed for all of us. I vote that we pull their heads off right now!

TOMATO 6: *(to PEA 3)* Oh yeah? Just you try it, you weedy little green thing! I'll uproot you so fast…

PEA 5: *(to TOMATO 6)* Oh will you? And just what do you think that will achieve?

TOMATO 6: *(to PEA 5)* Well, you won't be able to grow and we'll have this place all to ourselves again.

PEA 2: It's not our fault that we ended up here with you. Can't we just learn to get along together?

TOMATOES 1, 2, 4 & 5 and PEAS 1, 3, 5 & 6: *(in unison)* WHAT? IN THE SAME BED?!

Everyone starts talking and arguing at once, making lots of noise, when suddenly…

TOMATO 2: Humans!! Freeze!

---

*ALL of the PEAS and TOMATOES freeze and hold their positions.
MR and MRS JACKSON enter. They study the tomatoes and peas closely.*

Photocopiable

MRS JACKSON: Oh, look! The vegetables are growing. *(She takes a closer look.)* Just a minute! There's something wrong here, Brian.

MR JACKSON: *(looking at his feet)* I know, I know. I think I've put me wellies on the wrong feet.

MRS JACKSON: *(irritated)* Have you? Again? I'm beginning to think you prefer them that way! Anyway, I wasn't talking about that. It's these vegetables, they don't all look the same to me – do they to you?

MR JACKSON: Aah… No… Well… *(He points.)* These are peas and those are tomatoes.

MRS JACKSON: I thought so! What are they doing in the same bed?

MR JACKSON: *(helpfully)* Growing?

MRS JACKSON: *(sighing)* Yes, I can see that for myself. But why have you planted them like this? I don't remember Alan Titchmarsh suggesting this in his gardening book.

MR JACKSON: *(hopefully)* Would you believe me if I told you that I wanted to be the first with an unusual idea for vegetable gardening?

MRS JACKSON: No.

MR JACKSON: Oh. *(He pauses.)* Well, I suppose it'll have to be the truth then. *(He takes a deep breath.)* I dropped the seeds.

MRS JACKSON: Of course you did, that's how we've always planted them.

MR JACKSON: No. I DROPPED the seeds! I spilled them all when you made me jump when I was trying to decide which ones to put in. They went all over the place. I tried to pick them up but it only made things worse, so I left it. I didn't think it would matter.

Photocopiable

MRS JACKSON: *(crossly)* Oh no, why couldn't you have been more careful? Well, I don't suppose it will have to matter, will it? *(Then thinking about it)* We COULD pretend that we're trying new growing methods. *(She thinks again.)* Maybe I'll even write in and get a mention on 'Gardener's Question Time'. *(Dreamily)* That's been my life's ambition.

MR JACKSON looks at her as if he thinks this is a really weird ambition to have!

MRS JACKSON: So, that's decided then, we'll leave them to grow as they are and put the support canes in as usual. There's not much difference between peas and tomatoes, anyway.

MR JACKSON: All right. *(He has a good idea.)* Shall I jumble up the cabbage and cauliflowers as well?

MRS JACKSON: *(warning)* Steady on now, don't push it.

MR JACKSON: Okey dokey. Do you fancy a nice glass of wine?

MRS JACKSON: Yes, that'd be nice. The sun is over the yard arm, after all.

MR JACKSON: Yes. *(To MRS JACKSON in a puzzled voice)* What does that mean?

MRS JACKSON: Haven't got a clue…

MR and MRS JACKSON exit, chatting to each other.
The PEAS and TOMATOES unfreeze and all come to life again.

PEA 3: *(furious)* No difference between peas and tomatoes, indeed! What do they mean, no difference?!

TOMATO 6: *(angry)* How dare they!

PEA 5: *(offended)* How insulting!

TOMATO 4: *(angry)* There's a great deal of difference if you happen to be a tomato.

Photocopiable

PEA 1: *(angry)* Or a pea!

PEA 4: *(puzzled)* What's a 'yard arm'?

TOMATO 3: *(to PEA 4)* Yes, I was just wondering that, too…

TOMATO 1: *(to TOMATO 3 and PEA 4)* Well, it's…

PEA 6: *(interrupting quickly, scared)* Never mind all that! We've got a serious problem here! What are we gonna do? *(Wailing in fear again)* What are we gonna do? We're all doomed, doomed!

PEA 5: *(to PEA 6, angrily)* Will you stop that wailing! You're getting on my nerves. First sign of trouble and you start behaving like you're in a Greek tragedy. It really gets on my stalk!

PEA 1: *(to PEA 5 and PEA 6)* Look, stop it both of you! Why can't we just find a sensible solution? We've obviously been planted here by accident, and this is where we're going to have to stay. So why don't we just make the best of a bad situation and try to get along with each other?

ALL of the other PEAS and TOMATOES look at PEA 1 as if he/she is completely barmy.

TOMATO 6: *(sarcastic)* Yeah, right! Lovely sentiments. I'd like to echo them… *(pause)*… but I can't.

PEA 2: Why don't we just wait and see who grows the tallest, then whoever it is takes over the whole of the bed?

TOMATO 1: Great idea! The vegetable that takes up the most room wins!

TOMATO 4: *(to PEA 2 and TOMATO 1)* And just what do we do while we're waiting to grow?

PEA 2: *(to TOMATO 4)* Well, we… well, we… we… *(suddenly realizing that the plan won't work)*

Photocopiable

TOMATO 6: *(aggressively)* Why don't we just have a massive scrap and rip each other's flowers off and see who the winners are after that?

PEAS 3 & 5 and TOMATOES 2 & 4 agree and begin preparing themselves for a fight.

TOMATO 2: *(to TOMATO 6)* I don't think that's really sensible, is it? I mean, one of us might get hurt, and anyway *(pretending to yawn)* I'm feeling a little bit tired right now *(feeling his/ her head)* and I think I'm getting a headache and...

PEA 3: *(nastily to TOMATO 2)* Mangetout!

TOMATO 5: *(to PEA 3)* Who're you calling a 'mangetout'? If he doesn't want to fight – and I have to say I agree – then...

PEA 3: *(nastily again)* Mangetout! Mangetout! *(Mimicking Tomato 2 in a whining voice)* "I'm a likkle bit tired right now!"

PEA 5: *(laughing and also mimicking Tomato 2 in a whining voice)* "I think I'm getting a headache!"

ALL of the PEAS start laughing.

TOMATO 6: You just stop that! WE'RE not afraid of you lot! No way!

PEA 5: *(to TOMATO 6)* Oh yeah?!

TOMATO 6: *(to PEA 5)* Yeah!

TOMATO 3: *(nervously)* Well, I'm a little bit afraid...

TOMATO 4: *(to TOMATO 3)* Shut up! *(To the PEAS)* You lot take that back or there'll be trouble!

ALL of the PEAS now start chanting "Mangetout!", "Mangetout!" at the TOMATOES. A big fight begins.
The PEAS and TOMATOES are fighting as their characters indicate. The brave and bossy ones are really enjoying themselves; the lazy and scared ones are just tapping each other nervously and trying to look as if they are joining in.
Suddenly, whilst the fight is still happening, the RUNNER BEANS enter!

Photocopiable

RUNNER BEAN 1: *(talking like a gangster)* Hey! Hey! What's all this disturbance going on in our bed?

**RUNNER BEANS
2 & 3:** *(mean and nasty)* YEAH!

ALL of the TOMATOES and PEAS immediately stop fighting and turn, open-mouthed, to stare at the new arrivals.

ALL TOMATOES: *(in unison to the RUNNER BEANS)* YOUR bed?!

ALL PEAS: *(in unison to the RUNNER BEANS)* YOUR bed?!

RUNNER BEAN 1: Are you listening to me? That's what I said, didn't I? This is OUR bed. We saw it, we liked it and we've decided to stay.

PEA 5: And just who do you think you are?

RUNNER BEAN 2: We don't think, we KNOW that we're the runner beans.

RUNNER BEAN 3: *(nastily, pointing to RUNNER BEAN 1)* This here's our boss. *(Pointing to the PEAS and TOMATOES)* You're on our territory. *(Pointing to him/herself)* We're here to get rid of you – know what I mean?

RUNNER BEAN 2: *(thumping hand with fist menacingly)* We stand no nonsense from nobody. When we say move, you move. The boss likes it here, so here we stay – got it?!

RUNNER BEAN 2 & RUNNER BEAN 3 move to stand either side of RUNNER BEAN 1 and question him directly, whilst looking at the peas and tomatoes all the time.

RUNNER BEAN 3: Want me to snap their stalks, boss?

RUNNER BEAN 2: Want us to do 'em over like the other runner beans did to those carrots last week?

RUNNER BEAN 3: We can do it so it don't leave marks.

RUNNER BEAN 2: Yeah, not a scratch on them. Just frighten 'em a little, know what I mean, boss?

RUNNER BEAN 1: *(stopping them by raising his/her hands in a 'peaceful' gesture)* Beans, beans, easy now, back off. These good vegetables don't want violence. They'll move on without your 'friendly' persuasion. They understand what we're saying and I don't think you'll need to dirty your pretty little leaves. Save your special talents for another day. They understand *(to the PEAS and TOMATOES, menacingly)*, don't you?

PEA 6: *(wailing in terror)* Ooh! Now we're really in trouble! We're really doomed! Doomed!

PEA 5: *(to PEA 6)* Shut up! *(To the RUNNER BEANS)* Excuse us, just one moment before you rip us shoot from stalk, we've got to have a meeting. *(To the TOMATOES)* Are you with us on this?

TOMATO 1: Yeah! Come on tomatoes, gather round.

The TOMATOES and PEAS all form a group meeting away from the RUNNER BEANS.

TOMATO 2: So, what are we going to do? I've heard about these runner beans, they're a really nasty bunch, taking over wherever they go, terrorizing ordinary vegetables.

PEA 2: Yeah, and nothing's ever traced back to them, know what I mean? Healthy peas wither and die and no one is ever caught.

PEA 1: So how can we possibly beat them?

TOMATO 1: Well, first of all, I think we need to agree to work together on this.

There is a little pause whilst EVERYONE thinks about it.

TOMATO 1: So, are we all agreed?

Photocopiable

One or two of the vegetables hesitate and then everyone says:

ALL TOMATOES
& PEAS: Agreed.

TOMATO 1: Right! Now, what do runner beans need to have to keep going? To sustain their power?

PEA 4: More runner beans?

TOMATO 3: Fertilizer?

PEA 2: Little round stones?

TOMATO 2: Sunshine?

PEA 3: Whacking big sticks?

TOMATO 1: No, no, no! Think about it! What do we ALL need to be able to grow?

There is a pause whilst EVERYONE thinks about this.

TOMATO 4: I know! I know! I've got it! WATER! *(To TOMATO 1)* Right?

PEA 6: Oh, yeah, water. *(To TOMATO 4)* Well done!

TOMATO 4: *(showing off)* Well, I can't help being super intelligent. My great-great-grandmother was a champion prize-winning tomato, you know. I remember my mother telling me…

TOMATO 2: *(interrupting TOMATO 4)* All right! All right! Give it a rest! We've heard this story loads of times and it doesn't get any more interesting after the fourth or fifth telling!

PEA 4: I thought it sounded interesting.

TOMATO 2: Yes, well you two can have a little chat later, can't you? She'll be thrilled to find a new audience for her life story. If we still have a life to talk about, that is.

Photocopiable

PEA 1: Yes. Back to the matter in hand. So, the runner beans need water to keep going and the plan is…
…the plan is… *(slowly realizing)*… to cut off their water supply?!

TOMATO 1: Right!

TOMATO 3: Brilliant idea! *(Thinks hard about it)* So how do we stop it raining, then?

TOMATO 6: *(sighing)* We don't. We just suck up all the water from the ground and the runner beans won't be able to survive. They'll just wither and die.

PEA 2: Like so many of their innocent victims before them. Brilliant!

TOMATO 1: Right! So, are we all agreed that this is the plan? We drain every drop of water we can from the ground and get rid of those nasty runner beans for ever!

ALL of the other TOMATOES and PEAS nod their heads and murmur in agreement.

PEA 3: Let's go for it! I might not like sharing my bed with a bunch of tomatoes, but I'm certainly not going to let some beany-faced bullies trample all over me!

TOMATO 4: *(nodding in agreement)* I agree! I'm not going to be pushed around by some great stringy things who think they can scare anybody with their nasty bullying little ways!

PEA 6: They scared me!

PEA 5: *(to PEA 6)* Yes, well, let's be honest, your own shadow would make you turn mushy.

TOMATO 6: Are we all ready then? Off we go! Let's drain them till they drop!!

Photocopiable

EVERYONE moves back into their original positions and the action freezes in the positions of the PEAS and TOMATOES draining the soil dry.
The NARRATOR enters.

NARRATOR: In the face of a common enemy, the vegetables unite,
With red and green triumphantly fighting the good fight.
They pooled all their resources and sucked the soil dry
And saw the beans extinguished as they withered, flopped and died.

The RUNNER BEANS collapse slowly onto the stage and lie completely still, as if dead.
The PEAS and TOMATOES shake hands, congratulating each other silently, and then freeze again in the position of fully grown vegetables.

NARRATOR: From that day on they lived as friends and grew up tall and strong.
Apart from rows and arguments, they really got along;
And although they looked unusual, one green crop and one red,
They proved that different varieties can all live in one bed!

THE END

PRODUCTION SUPPORT

AUDITIONS AND CASTING

The easiest way to begin the audition process is to read the play through with the children two or three times. The initial reading should simply be an exercise in familiarizing the children with the material. The second read-through should enable children to volunteer to read specific character parts, and the third should be used for you to nominate specific children to read certain character parts. During the second and third reading, encourage the children to think about using vocal expression, following the stage directions and picking up their cues quickly, and write yourself notes about how the children perform when reading specific roles. At any read-through you must give every child a chance to read something.

It is important to make a concerted effort to allow poor readers a chance to read, and encourage others in the group to show patience and consideration when they are listening. Plays always help poor readers to develop their language skills, and their enthusiasm in wanting to perform often leads to a great deal of work away from the rehearsals to ensure that they know their lines. A poor reader does not necessarily make a poor actor.

There are several alternatives for casting your play and the process can be as formal or informal as you wish.

FORMAL AUDITIONS

These can be held by selecting specific speeches or scenes from the play and asking the children to either learn or read them through in various group combinations. The drawback of this is that it takes an inordinate amount of time to plan and execute and makes children very tense and often unable to perform well, especially if their memory skills are not strong.

CHILDREN CHOOSING THEIR OWN ROLES

Another option is to ask the children to write, confidentially, on pieces of paper their first and second role choices. Ask them to try to make sure the spellings are correct and to add their names and surnames to their slips of paper. Some children will only have one choice of role, others will all go for the same first choice and there will be some children who 'don't care' what role they are given!

Gather all the pieces of paper together and, in a quiet place at another time, sit down and work out who wants what and which role combinations would work. Try to be as fair to both the children and the play as possible. Children are often aware of their 'failings' as actors and usually accept that others have stronger performance skills, but this doesn't prevent many children from feeling acute disappointment if they fail to secure the role they are desperate for.

The War of the
Vegetables

When allocating roles after using this method, ask the children to sit in a circle and read from the bottom of the cast list upwards, giving the name of the character followed by the name of the child who has been given the part. Sometimes a little of what is known as 'director speak' comes in useful, such as trying to convince upset children that they are more suited to smaller 'character roles' than to a main part.

After each part has been given out, allow the children up to 5 minutes to discuss the casting and to accept and compare their roles.

DRAWING NAMES OUT OF A HAT

Another method which is fairer, but more risky for your play, is to ask the children to put their names into a hat and to draw a name for each character. Children have mixed feelings about this process: there is always the possibility that their name will be drawn for the character they want to play, but they know that this is not guaranteed. Also, less confident children occasionally end up with large roles which they really don't feel happy with or comfortable performing.

CHOOSING ACTORS YOURSELF

The final option is to simply allocate the roles yourself, choosing children that you know are able and confident. However, this can upset a number of other children who are rarely given the opportunity to perform, and removes any sense of the children being involved in the casting process at all. It can also cause feelings of resentment among the cast, which could then affect the success of the production.

After a number of years and a number of arguments, floods of tears and several very unhappy children, I have reached the conclusion that the second option – children choosing their own roles – is the fairest choice. It gives children a chance to specify which roles they would like to perform, given a choice, and allows you the opportunity to make the final decision in a considered manner. It always surprises me which parts children choose to go for, and which appear to be the most popular! Sometimes children who appear confident – and who might have otherwise been given a major role – select small parts, and sometimes the reverse happens, with less confident children being very keen to take on a demanding role.

I feel strongly that enthusiasm for playing a particular part will result in an an eagerness to learn lines, a willingness to take on a role wholeheartedly and an easier rehearsal process, and I have been justified in this belief over and over again when 'risking' a major part on a child who may not have been given a chance had I chosen a different casting method.

Whichever casting method you choose, you should then ask the children to sit in a circle again, arranging them according to character or family groups. Then read through the play one more time to get the feel of how it sounds with the roles established.

Finally, tell the children that each person in the cast is as important as the next and that, without one character, you don't have a full team and, therefore, a complete play. They won't believe you – they've already spent time counting the number of lines they have to say – but it is true and needs to be expressed!

DIRECTOR SPEAK

Whatever decisions you make about casting, and however fair you try to be, there are going to be children who are upset when the parts are distributed. Many children feel that they never have the opportunity to show what they can do; some can build up quite a strong resentment against others who always seem to get the main roles, and quieter children can feel a sense of failure at not having pushed themselves forward again.

These feelings need to be dealt with as sensitively and as quickly as possible, away from the main group. In these situations you must employ what is known as 'director speak', in an attempt to pacify, boost and reassure the children. This consists of using a variety of statements aimed to placate, for example:

● *I know you're upset about not getting the part you wanted, but I really needed a good actor for the part I have given you to encourage all of the others to perform well in that scene.*
● *I understand that you wanted a main part, but you read this part so well that I just had to give it to you.*
● *I appreciate that you're disappointed, but I wanted to give you the chance to try something different this time, to show me what you could do.*
● *I know that you're unhappy, but can you understand that I have to be fair to everyone and give others a chance to try a bigger part sometimes?*

And others of a similar nature. The children will probably recognize that you are trying to pacify them, but what is important about using 'director speak' is that you are hearing and acknowledging their feelings of unhappiness and that they have had the opportunity to express them.

Whatever you say isn't going to make a lot of difference for some children, and in these cases they need to be given the direct choice of either playing the part they have been given or not being in the play at all, however cruel it may seem. Most children will choose the former. Any child opting out of the play should be occupied with other tasks, such as painting scenery, prompting, or making props and costumes. They will often regret their decision to pull out and, if possible, should be given the chance to join in again.

The main issue which angers and upsets children is feeling a sense of unfairness about the part allocation. Therefore if, when using 'director speak' on a previous occasion, you promised a bigger part next time, you must fulfil your promise. Also, if you have stated that 'everyone needs to be given a chance', then don't under any circumstances allocate the main roles to the same children as were chosen last time.

I use 'director speak' all the time and try to be reasonable, fair and understanding in the way that I use it. In that context, it works.

STRUCTURING REHEARSALS

When faced with directing a play, it is sometimes difficult to know what to tackle first. You have a large group of children awaiting your instructions, a limited amount of access to the school hall and very little time! Good pre-rehearsal planning and preparation is, therefore, essential. The following timetable has always worked for me and it might be suitable for you, too.

REHEARSALS 1 TO 3

These should be used to complete what is known as 'blocking' – that is, simply specifying the movements of children on, off and around the stage. Explain your staging ideas to the cast, marking out the stage area and exits using chairs, tell them what furniture and scenery will be on stage and use chairs or other equipment to represent this as well. Take time to ensure that all of the children in the cast are familiar with the setting, acting arena and their movements before continuing. They'll be desperate to get on with the 'acting' but it is essential that they understand the space they are working in and know their moves before going any further. It is impossible to teach children to act and give them instructions about where to enter and exit at the same time.

STAGE 1

Immediately after casting, spend an hour or two resolving practicalities – what sort of stage the play will be performed on, how many entrances and exits you'll have and where these will be (plus consideration of what imaginary setting lies beyond them, if relevant), where the children will go when they are not on stage, exactly how and where each character enters and exits, what scenery, furniture and props you will have, if any, and where these will be positioned on the stage, whether any characters will enter from other parts of the auditorium and, if so, how.

All of these points need to be clearly defined to your own satisfaction before starting rehearsals.

REHEARSALS 4 TO 8

Break the play down into small sections and rehearse these individually. Don't try to work through the whole play at a single rehearsal at this point. Start from the beginning and work through a maximum of three scenes. Rehearse the same section a number of times until you feel that 'familiarity is breeding contempt' and then move on to the next section.

Continue the following rehearsal from where you left off – never repeat the previous section and then move on, or the result will be one or two sections that are absolutely brilliant and a number that are completely under-rehearsed (I speak from experience!). This will mean that some children are unoccupied for some of the rehearsals. Set them learning their lines in pairs; watching the play and making notes, giving you feedback about how it looks; making props; designing posters and programmes, and so on. Insist that they remain aware of what is going on – they could be called to rehearsal at any time!

Continue rehearsing the play in small sections until you have completed the whole script. Make notes as you're going along of any potential difficulties, areas, scenes or characters which you feel will need extra rehearsing and ideas that you have for scenery, props, costumes, effects and so on.

REHEARSALS 9 TO 11

Rehearse the complete play at each rehearsal. Use these rehearsals to concentrate on scenes or sections which need extra attention. Try to get through the whole play at least once during each rehearsal period, but don't panic if you fail to do so. Again, never go back over sections, always start the next rehearsal from the point at which you finished during the last one.

REHEARSALS 12 TO 14

These should be used for complete run-throughs – a technical rehearsal to include any lights, sound, props, music or special effects you might be including, and two dress rehearsals complete with costumes and make-up. Spend 10 minutes at the beginning of the final rehearsal to work out and practise your 'curtain call' and then run through the play completely without stopping. Final rehearsals are always a nightmare – the children are stressed and excited, you're stressed and beginning to panic and everyone seems to be snapping at each other! Try to keep children occupied at all times, plan what you want to achieve in the rehearsals and try to stick to your plan.

I appreciate that this is the rehearsal structure for the 'ideal world' and it doesn't take into account those little things sent to try us: children being absent, falling out, not learning their lines, forgetting everything they learned at the last rehearsal, the props and costumes failing to materialize, and so on, but those stresses are what give us the sense of achievement when the play finally goes on – and it does always go on, despite the horrendous feeling that it will fail. The old saying 'it'll be all right on the night' usually applies!

STAGING AND SCENERY

The War of the Vegetables is very simple to stage. It was first performed on a proscenium arch stage (a square, raised stage which resembles a box, with structured spaces at the side for 'wings' and full curtains). There was no set at all, the stage was completely bare, and the characters simply walked or jumped on from the wings at the side of the stage to make their entrances and exited in the same manner.

If you want to be adventurous, you can draw pictures of flowers and vegetables and fix them to any back wall you may have (on a proscenium arch stage this is known as the cyclorama, or cyc).

If you are performing the play on raised rostra – as many schools do – then create simple screens to act

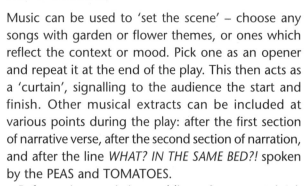

as the wings at the side of the stage and decorate them with pictures of flowers and vegetables to represent the garden.

The narrator(s) does not necessarily have to speak his/her lines from the stage; he/she can do this from any part of the hall, and this can create an interesting diversion for the audience.

LIGHTING

Lighting in a play should be used to establish time, enhance setting or create atmosphere. If you are lucky enough to have a professional lighting rig, you can create some really wonderful lighting effects. If not, simple lighting can often be sufficient to establish the basics. *The War of the Vegetables* can be lit very simply with what is known as a 'general wash', which just gives an overall lighted area for the actors.

For this simple lighting plot, flood the stage on very slightly dimmed lights for the initial setting, when MR JACKSON drops the seeds, then bring them up to full effect just before the vegetables enter – to indicate the arrival of better weather and sunnier days! The lights can then be left at this level throughout the rest of the play. If you don't have the facilities to dim lights at all, simply leave them on full for the whole play.

For a stage with no front curtains, lights can also be used to black out the stage during scene changes, or in preparation for the 'curtain call'.

MUSIC AND SOUND EFFECTS

Music can be used to 'set the scene' – choose any songs with garden or flower themes, or ones which reflect the context or mood. Pick one as an opener and repeat it at the end of the play. This then acts as a 'curtain', signalling to the audience the start and finish. Other musical extracts can be included at various points during the play: after the first section of narrative verse, after the second section of narration, and after the line *WHAT? IN THE SAME BED?!* spoken by the PEAS and TOMATOES.

Before using music in a public performance, check that your school has the relevant licences to broadcast music at a public event.

Alternatively, the children can sing songs themselves – if you don't want your actors to sing, other children in the school can be utilized as a chorus, seated around the staging area, and can sing the songs whilst those on stage mime appropriate actions.

PROPS

Again, this play is very simple to stage and the only props which are essential are the packets of seeds for MR JACKSON to carry on with him at his first entrance! Nothing else is essential, although a few gardening tools scattered around might create a nice effect.

COSTUMES

Costumes for *The War of the Vegetables* are also very simple. If you have the time and skill to create elaborate costumes, then go to town on leaves, stalks and flower heads! If not, the following ideas can work perfectly well:

Mr Jackson: He should be dressed as a stereotypical farmer – complete with wellington boots and a cap. The child playing this role must remember to put his/her wellingtons on the wrong feet! A pair of jeans and a checked shirt will be perfectly adequate for this role.

Narrator: The narrator should be dressed in his/her own, smart, clothes. If using more than one narrator, it is better to stipulate a colour scheme – either all in black and white or red and black, or similar. This is so that they are dressed in some form of recognizable 'costume' and, more importantly, that they feel they are. Narrators need the thrill of 'dressing up' too! Alternatively, the Narrators can be dressed in suitable 'character' costumes.

Mrs Jackson: She should be dressed in a stereotypical skirt, blouse and – optionally – a headscarf. I leave this as an option because sometimes wearing a headscarf can prevent children from being able to hear properly! Shoes for Mrs Jackson can be a problem unless you have a mother with small feet or a child with large feet! Otherwise, I'd use black or brown brogues, or black pumps or ballet shoes and dress them up with ribbon.

Peas: Use the same costume items as for the tomatoes, but dress them all in green!

Tomatoes: Dress them all in red: leggings, jogging bottoms or tights (with the feet cut off) combined with T-shirts, sweatshirts, jumpers or tops. Try to keep their feet bare if possible, as they have to enter by jumping onto the stage, which can be dangerous in slippery tights or socks. Jumpers should only be worn in an emergency, if nothing else is available – the combination of heat and excitement can make children physically ill and I've known one or two to faint!

Effective stalks for the tomatoes can be created in the following way: cut two petal shapes out of green tissue paper, crêpe paper or a green plastic bag; place these on top of each other, with the top petals fitting between the gaps in the bottom one; grip them into place in the child's hair or, alternatively, cut two slots in the centre and thread through some green ribbon, tying it under the child's chin. (The latter is a better method as it makes the stalk stick up from the head.)

Runner beans: They should be dressed in green leggings and tops but should be given black jackets to wear and dark sunglasses. This is to give the impression that they are gangsters or thugs! If they have smart black shoes which are not too modern, these would complete the image but, if not, black pumps will work fine. If they do wear smart shoes, give them green or brown socks to wear as well.

MAKE-UP

All make-up is dependent on the type of lighting used in your performance arena. If you are working under professional stage lights, then more must be applied, as they remove colour and contour from the face. If, however, you are working under school lights or strip lights, be very careful just to define features and express the characters.

Any base or foundation should be applied all over the face and neck area, including the ears and the back of the neck. A small amount of make-up must also be used to cover any other areas of bare flesh, such as arms and hands. For large expanses like these, water-based make-up is the fastest and most effective. It is important to cover all 'bare flesh' areas, especially if working under professional theatre lighting, as the lights will show very clearly the distinction between made-up and non-made-up flesh.

Water-based cake make-up, or face paint, needs to be applied with a sponge which is barely damp and fully covered with make-up. If you have too much water on your sponge, the make-up will streak and application will be patchy. If you decide to use grease sticks to create a base or foundation, select a brick red and a colour paler than the child's skin; apply this pale colour all over the face first, blending well with your fingers, and then dot the red on forehead, cheeks, chin and nose, and blend it in thoroughly and carefully. The face should then have a good foundation base on which you can apply other colours. If not, keep adding more of either colour and blending thoroughly until you are happy with the result. Use the same technique for all other areas of bare skin. 'Set' any grease make-up with a light dusting of loose powder to keep it in place under the hot stage lights.

Take care when applying blusher using a grease stick – a little goes a long way. Grease sticks for eyeshadow come in a variety of colours – not just blue! – and any of these can be used to make up your characters.

Try to avoid using ordinary make-up for the stage; it isn't suitable and rarely withstands the heat, often fading within a few moments of being applied. Theatre make-up is specifically designed for the stage and it's worth spending £20 or £30 on purchasing a good selection of proper theatrical make-up.

Other items which would be useful for your make-up box include: hair gel, talcum powder (for whitening hair), a stipple brush (or small blusher brush) and black grease stick for creating facial stubble, fake hair and spirit gum for applying it, cocktail sticks for creating age lines, teeth blackout liquid, coloured hair spray and glitter gels.

One final point: it is important to practise applying the make-up prior to the performances.

The make-up for *The War of the Vegetables* can be very simple. The following ideas can be used:

Narrator: Narrators should be made up with simple, light lipstick and eyeshadow. Try to prevent them from wearing too much as it isn't necessary. It's more important that they look clean, tidy and smart on stage.

Tomatoes and Peas: The tomatoes and peas only need red or green circles on their cheeks and red or green make-up on their eyelids. You don't need to cover their faces completely and doing this can cause all sorts of problems as, once you start, every bit of bare flesh has to be coloured!

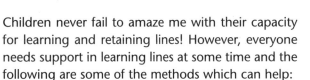

LEARNING LINES

Children never fail to amaze me with their capacity for learning and retaining lines! However, everyone needs support in learning lines at some time and the following are some of the methods which can help:

REPETITION

This requires constant and regular reading of the script. Go over their lines again and again, and they'll learn them by rote. Using this method means that children often learn everyone else's lines as well, which is not a problem until they insist on prompting while on stage!

FROM CUES

Read the line immediately before theirs. Let them read their line out loud. Read the 'cue line' again, but this time cover up their line. This way, they are learning the important cues as well as their own lines.

ON PAPER

Write the cue lines and their own lines on a separate piece of paper, to prevent them being daunted by a large script. Use this method for children to learn one scene or short section at a time. They can carry the pieces of paper around with them wherever they go, and will memorize the lines quite quickly by absorbing these short extracts.

ON TAPE

Help the children to read through the script two or three times. Record their cue lines on tape, leaving a long pause after each one for them to interject with their own lines. Work through this with them initially, using the script as an accompanying visual aid, then let them try it alone. Gradually remove their dependence on using the script, until they can say their lines in the pauses on the tape without hesitating.

Alternatively, record cue lines and their lines and then leave a gap for them to repeat their own lines.

VERBAL SUPPORT/ADULT HELPERS

Some children respond better to verbal support, and learn lines by hearing them spoken and then simply repeating them. This can take up an awful lot of your rehearsal time, though! Use this method to also ensure that children recognize words in the script and can pronounce them.

Enlist the support of family members to help the children with learning their lines. Encourage children to 'test' each other, and try to create an atmosphere of support. Don't be too worried if children paraphrase, so long as important aspects of the script aren't omitted!

Mr and Mrs Jackson: They need a little bit of foundation all over their faces, blue eyeshadow, a touch of blusher and a nice red or pink lipstick for Mrs Jackson. If you want to give Mr Jackson a bit of stubble, take a small, firm brush – a blusher brush works well – cover it with black make-up (a black grease stick or similar) and tap it lightly end-on onto the face. Ask the child to suck his/her lips in and apply just below the nose as well. Children will moan whilst it's being applied, but they will love the end result.

Runner beans: The runner beans should have the same make-up as the peas, with the addition of green lips – to give an unpleasant shape and hue to their mouths!

IN A WHOLE GROUP

Use what literacy time you can to read through the script a number of times as a whole group. Try to balance the need for the children to remember what they have to say, with not frightening them so much that they forget everything! Children should, however, be made aware of the fact that they will not be able to take their scripts – or pieces of paper – onto the stage with them. This should be made clear as early on in the rehearsal process as possible, so that they all understand what is expected of them.

The most secure approach is to ensure that the children know and, if possible, learn the whole script, as this builds knowledge of what should happen in each scene and means that the children can improvise or say another character's lines if something goes wrong.

LINE-LEARN REHEARSALS

If you have the time, include in your rehearsal schedule one or two line-learning sessions: sit with the children in a circle, positioning them in character order, and tell them to recite the whole play without looking at their scripts, which they should place face down on the floor in front of them. This can help the person prompting to appreciate his or her job, too. It also provides you with an awareness of which actors need more help with learning their lines.

PROMPTERS

Prompters should be instructed to give just the first word of a sentence, only supplying more words if the actor is still struggling. Ensure that only one person is responsible for prompting, and give them every opportunity to practise their skill.

REHEARSALS WITHOUT SCRIPTS

It is a good idea to advise the children of a specific day by which they must have learned all of their lines. Tell them which rehearsal this will be and stick to it! At that rehearsal, don't allow any children to go on with their scripts in hand. It will be a slow, painful process and the prompter will work overtime, but it is a necessary evil! Scripts are like security blankets and all actors panic when they are taken away. Try to intersperse these 'no scripts' rehearsals with additional 'line-learn' rehearsals to boost their confidence.

Note: never allow children to write lines on parts of their anatomy. If any child comes to a rehearsal with lines written on the palms of their hands, for example, insist that they wash them off. When they do remember their lines, when the play goes on, they will feel a far greater sense of achievement than if they had simply read them. It is not acceptable to have lines written down anywhere on the actor's

person, or on pieces of paper situated on the stage, and children must realize this. It's also very risky – what happens if you lose your place while reading, the lines fade from your skin, or someone moves your piece of paper!

CALMING NERVES AND CHANNELLING ENERGY

Those children who become stressed and nervous about performing must be allowed to feel as if they have a 'get out clause'. If possible, have another child in mind ready to take over their lines and let them know that they don't have to perform if they really don't want to. I say this on a regular basis to the young children I direct and, however terrified they become, they always end up performing. I think this is because they know that taking part in the play is their choice and that they can pull out at any time.

Give 'energetic' (a euphemism for 'disruptive'!) children specific tasks to perform. I often involve these children in helping others to learn lines, making props and even applying make-up during rehearsals. Having a sense of responsibility about an important job will usually calm children who become overexcited. However, there is always the option of threatening to remove them from the play – and meaning it – if they don't calm down.

The trick is to try to keep children occupied, to prevent them from having the time to be worried and to use up spare energy! Use your rehearsal planning time to add two or three production-related tasks which can be done while rehearsals are in progress. Alternatively, take drawing paper and crayons to rehearsals and ask children to draw the stage and set. I've also used word puzzles and colouring books and asked them to write and decorate invitations to their families to come and see the play. All obvious strategies, but they work!

CURTAIN CALLS

I've seen some terrible curtain calls which have completely spoiled an otherwise good performance. Bear in mind that this is the last memory your audience will have of the play, and that any sloppiness will completely override any professionalism which may have gone before!

I'm not in favour of the 'pantomime-style' walk-down curtain calls in which the actors come on to take their bows one by one, to the differing responses of the audience. It isn't fair for those children who have taken on the less 'popular' parts.

A good way of structuring curtain calls is as follows:

● Line all of the children in rows on stage in height order – tallest ones at the back. Space them out so that they can all be seen.
● Tell them to look around and make a note of who they are standing next to, in front of and behind.

● Instruct all of the children to stand upright with their feet together and their hands resting lightly on the front of their thighs.
● Now nominate one child in the centre of the front row to start the bow. Tell all of the other children to watch this child carefully, without making their observations noticeable.
● When the nominated child on the front row bows slowly, everyone must bow. Bowing should be done from the waist, with hands sliding down to the knees. Make sure everyone travels at the same, slow pace – bowing too quickly can give the appearance of a group of nodding ducks!
● Tell the children to hold the bowing position for a slow count of 'two', then everyone should straighten up again.
● Repeat, with everyone following the front row leader again.

Finally – and essentially – make sure that the children retain the same level of professionalism when leaving the stage. Don't allow them to scream, shout, wave to their mums or anything else!

A smooth, professional ending like this can really round off a lovely performance.

The War of the Vegetables

LITERACY SUPPORT

The following range of ideas for literacy teaching are based on reading and performing the playscript.

STORY

Ask the children to retell the story. This can be done in a number of contexts:

- orally – assign sections to different groups and invite retelling in sequence, with the whole class as audience
- by storyboarding main events, with or without captions, in small groups or as a whole class
- by individual children recording main incidents in single sentences and drawing accompanying pictures to create a 'wall story'.

Devise an alternative ending to the play, working as a whole class or in small groups, and ask the children to improvise it before recording it in writing or on tape.

Help the children to clap the rhythm of the narrator's poetry and encourage them to use it as a model to write their own poetry.

CHARACTERS

Ask the children to choose their favourite character from the play to draw.

Each child can then add the character's name above his/her drawing and write three words underneath it to describe the character.

Let the children perform the play using simple puppets, paying particular attention to the voices for different characters and the narrator.

THEME

What is the main theme of the play? Is it like any other plays or stories the children have read? Ask them to record their thoughts in writing and draw comparisons.

As a class, explore the dilemma facing the vegetables, and work with the children to come up with alternative solutions.

WORKING WITH PLAYSCRIPT LAYOUT

Using a short section of text, explore the conventions of layout for playscripts. Point out the use of brackets, italic for stage directions, the structuring of scenes, and so on.

Let the children practise laying out a playscript on a computer, transposing a familiar story into scripted format. Provide them with one or two pages taken from the playscript of *The War of the Vegetables* on photocopiable pages 19–35 to use as a model.

PERFORMANCE-RELATED TASKS

Invite the children to write and design a poster advertising a performance of the play, persuading friends and family to come. Or they could write and design a programme for the play which gives all the relevant information to the audience.